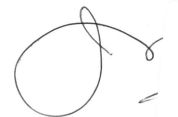

HYMN PRELUDES

for Lent, Holy Week and Easter

Rosalie Bonighton
Paul Bryan
Andrew Fletcher
Andrew Gant
Colin Hand
Richard Lloyd
Colin Mawby
Andrew Moore
June Nixon
James Patten
Noel Rawsthorne
Richard Shephard
Christopher Tambling
Alan Viner

Kevin Mayhew

12-99

We hope you enjoy the music in
Hymn Preludes for Lent, Holy Week and Easter.
Further copies of this and other outstanding collections of organ music
are available from your local music shop or Christian bookshop.

In case of difficulty, please contact the publisher direct by writing to:

The Sales Department
KEVIN MAYHEW LTD
Rattlesden
Bury St Edmunds
Suffolk IP30 0SZ

Phone 01449 737978
Fax 01449 737834

Please ask for our complete catalogue of Church Music.

Front Cover: *Christ and Mary Magdalene* by Jan Brueghel *(1568-1625)*
Reproduced by kind permission of Rafael Valls Gallery, London.

Cover designed by Veronica Ward and Graham Johnstone

First published in Great Britain in 1995 by Kevin Mayhew Ltd

ISBN 0 86209 730 4
Catalogue No: 1400071

Music Editors: Rosalind Dean and Tamzin Howard
Music setting by Rosalind Dean

Printed and bound in Great Britain

Contents

Page

LENT

HOLY WEEK

EASTER

THIS JOYFUL EASTERTIDE

James Patten

VICTORY
Colin Hand

for Howard Hollis

AUS DER TIEFE

June Nixon

Pained (♩ = 52)

11

ST FULBERT

Richard Lloyd

14

for Billy

ST ALBINUS

Paul Bryan

GELOBT SEI GOTT

Andrew Gant

Allegro spirituoso

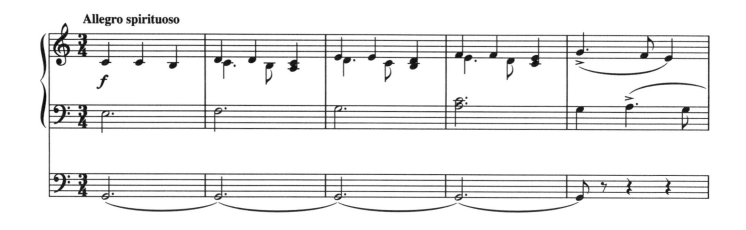

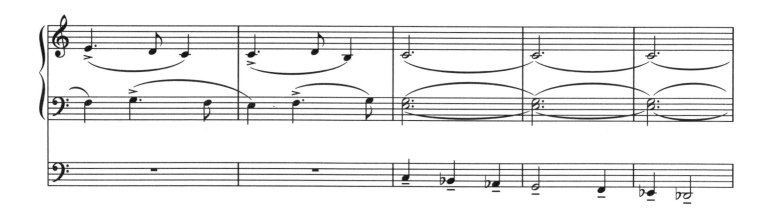

20

O FILII ET FILIAE

Colin Mawby

STOCKTON

Noel Rawsthorne

27

EASTER HYMN

Christopher Tambling

29

NOEL NOUVELET

Alan Viner

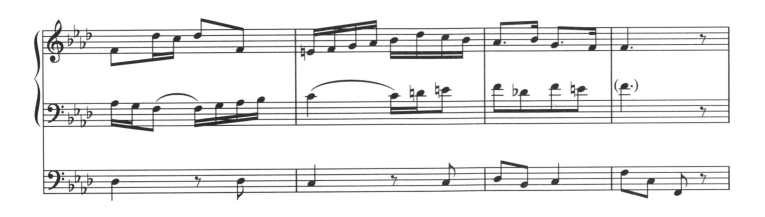

32

WERE YOU THERE

Christopher Tambling

HERONGATE

James Patten

poco rit.

a niente

39

CASWALL

Richard Lloyd

42

43

LUX EOI

Dom Andrew Moore

SOUTHWELL

Colin Hand

Andante con rubato ($\quad$ = c.72)

WÜRTTEMBERG

Richard Lloyd

Tempo comodo

allargando   a tempo

cresc.

49

poco allargando

50

a tempo

allargando

a tempo

poco allargando

51

a tempo

poco allargando

a tempo

53

HORSLEY

Richard Shephard

MACCABAEUS

Noel Rawsthorne

ST THOMAS

Andrew Gant

ABRIDGE

Colin Mawby

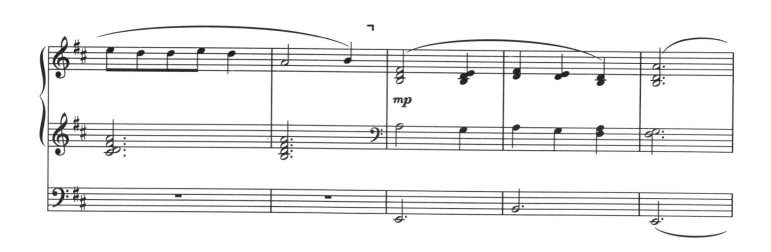

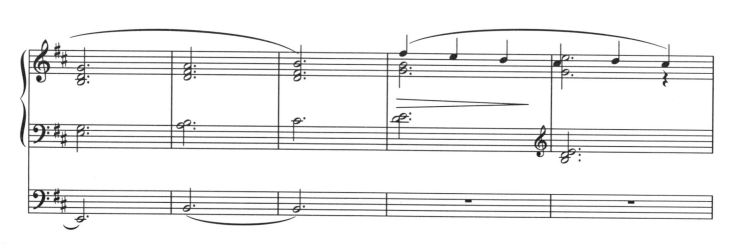

64

SAVANNAH

Rosalie Bonighton

STABAT MATER

Alan Viner

Andante flessibile ($\quarternote$ = 68)

Sw. *mp*

16'+8'+ Sw.

poco rit.

ST JOHN DAMASCENE

Noel Rawsthorne

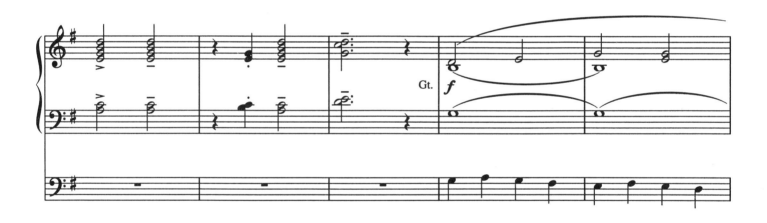

73

Tubas or Sw.

Gt.

74

ROCKINGHAM
Rosalie Bonighton

PASSION CHORALE

Andrew Fletcher

WINCHESTER NEW

Dom Andrew Moore

ST THEODULPH

Colin Hand

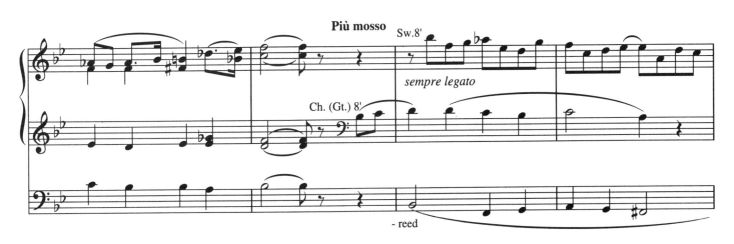

for Howard Hollis

ELLACOMBE

June Nixon

for Gudrun on the occasion of her Confirmation

ST BERNARD

Paul Bryan

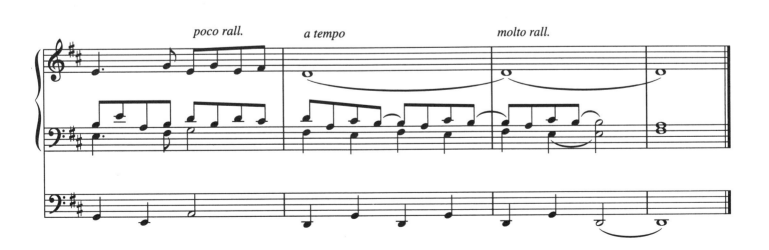

SALZBURG

Andrew Fletcher

Maestoso, ben articolato (♩ = 60)

Solo reed **ff**

rit.

a tempo

Allargando

ff

*Optional

About the Composers

Rosalie Bonighton is a recitalist, teacher and composer with a special interest in writing music for new liturgical needs.

Paul Bryan (*b.*1950) is Director of Music of St John's College School, Cambridge, where he also conducts the Walmisley Singers.

Andrew Fletcher (*b.*1950) is a teacher, composer, accompanist and recitalist, performing regularly all over the world.

Andrew Gant (*b.*1963) is Director of Music in Chapel at Selwyn College, Cambridge. He also directs the *Light Blues* vocal ensemble and is Musical Director of the Thursford Christmas concerts. He has worked extensively as an arranger for both radio and television.

Colin Hand (*b.*1929) is a composer of choral, orchestral and chamber music for both professional and amateur players.

Richard Lloyd (*b.*1933) was Assistant Organist of Salisbury Cathedral and successively Organist of Hereford and Durham Cathedrals. He now divides his time between examining and composing.

Colin Mawby (*b.*1936) composes in many forms. He was previously Choral Director at Radio Telefís Éireann, the national broadcasting authority in the Republic of Ireland, and Master of the Music at Westminster Cathedral.

Dom Andrew Moore (*b.*1936) is a Benedictine Monk at Downside Abbey, near Bath.

June Nixon is Organist and Director of the Choir at St Paul's Cathedral, Melbourne, Australia. She also teaches at the Melbourne University School of Music.

James Patten (*b.*1936) is a composer and conductor who has held a variety of lecturing posts at Universities and Colleges, including Professor of Composition at Trinity College of Music.

Noel Rawsthorne (*b.*1929) was Organist of Liverpool Cathedral for twenty-five years and City Organist and Artistic Director at St George's Hall, Liverpool. He was also Senior Lecturer in Music at St Katharine's College Liverpool until his retirement in 1993. In 1994 he was recently awarded an honorary degree of Doctor of Music by the University of Liverpool

Richard Shephard (*b.*1949) is Headmaster of the Minster School, York and Vicar Choral in York Minster. He has served on the Archbishops' Commission on Church Music and on the Archbishops' Commission on Cathedrals.

Christopher Tambling (*b.*1964) is the Director of Music at Glenalmond College in Perthshire.

Alan Viner (*b.*1951) was formerly Director of Music at the Priory Boys' Grammar School, Shrewsbury, and the Wakeman School, Shrewsbury. He now devotes his time to private teaching, composing and accompanying.